PRAISE FOR JOHNNY WANDER:

... a lovely, easy, enjoyable read ... These are the kind of people you want to bump into and spend time with, but if that never happens, the comic is an excellent substitute.

– Nina Stone,
The Factual Opinion

"[Johnny Wander] balances the every day with the surreal and somehow manages to make even the mundane seem fantastic, not to mention some absolutely lovely, and intriguing artwork. I wish I had a bit more Johnny Wander in my own life!"

– Emma Claire Goodman,
BUST Magazine

Best Thing
I Read This Week

– Whitney Matheson
USA TODAY's POP CANDY

"Johnny Wander is consistently funny and sweet ... there's alway a sense of joy in a Johnny Wander strip, even if it's one that ends in disaster."

– Greg McElhatton,
Read About Comics

The best comic on the internet ... ACTUALLY, the best comic in the world!!

– Ananth's Mom,
about the only comic she reads

"What Yuko Ota and Ananth Panagariya have created is nothing less than a more modern, authentic-feeling, young-adult ... version of Archie ... It's self-contained, self-explanatory, and above all, as accessible to the first time reader as to the obsessive fan. ... And that's what ... sets Johnny Wander, essentially an autobio webcomic, apart from most of its contemporaries."

– Gary Tyrell,
FLEEN.COM

JOHNNY WANDER VOLUME 3: THE BALLAD OF LAUNDRY CAT

Written with the lightness of a breeze by Ananth Panagariya.
Illustrated with fighting spirit by Yuko Ota.

Indispensable people: George Rohac, Conrad Kreyling, John Arthur Kelly, Evan
Dahm, Lela Graham and our parents. Couldn't do it without you.

First edition: November 2012.
ISBN-10: 0-9785016-4-8
ISBN-13: 978-0-9785016-4-8

5 4 3 2 1

Printed in the U.S.A.

Portions of this book are published online at www.johnnywander.com. This
volume collects the Johnny Wander comics posted online between January 11,
2011 and July 17, 2012 (with some minor exceptions).

This book is dedicated to

FOREWORD

Yuko and Ananth are good cooks.

I know this not because JOHNNY WANDER's anecdotes are sometimes about dinner and bread machines; I know it because of what they choose to leave in. Or out.

First thing I leaned to make were stews. Throw it all inna pot and see what you've got. And casseroles. Throw it all inna dish, ladle some carbs over the top, and see whatcha got. And pizza. Spread the leftover stew on the dough, dump cheese on till you can't see the leftovers anymore, bake it. Then see whatcha got. And that's what I did in my writing as well: what am I interested in? Throw it all in there and see what happens. Whatcha got? A very tasty mess. But a mess just the same.

Messes are delicious, yes, but they get better with care. Don't throw in everything you've got; how much of this vegetable, that spice, that protein? What kind of broth? What was missing from that last pot, that made it seem not as good as it could be? Did the plot drag, did we not understand why the main character refused to make a choice? Would everything have gone better with a bit more humor? More spice?

Many of the best autobiographical comics are stews, rich and deep and full of experience. But there's more than stew to good cooking. I have heard light entertainments referred to as 'trivial souffles,' but any cook will tell you, the making of a souffle is not simple. Considerable skill is required. Some of the most amazing dishes have only a few ingredients. Yuko and Ananth have made some conscious choices of topics in JOHNNY WANDER: stuff to leave out, stuff to leave in. Stuff to focus on. There are many, many autobio comics about deep topics and raw subjects and sometimes they have Too Much Information and sometimes they make your eyes burn. There aren't very many which are having so much fun with lighter fare. Sometimes you want a big bowl of everything. But sometimes you just want a cookie or a slice of really amazing bread. I have no doubt that when these two turn to short story comics or long-form novel comics or avant-garde experimentation that they will bring great skill, forethought, and refinement to them. And charm and wit and style. And power.

I need to make some cookies now.

Carla Speed McNeil,
slop-and-dump cook of FINDER

LIGHTSPEEDPRESS.COM
FINDERCOMICS.COM

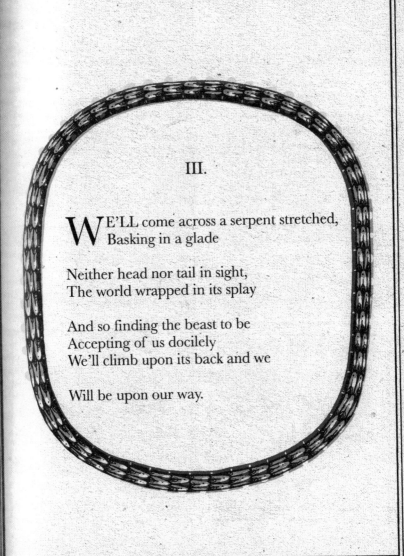

III.

WE'LL come across a serpent stretched,
Basking in a glade

Neither head nor tail in sight,
The world wrapped in its splay

And so finding the beast to be
Accepting of us docilely
We'll climb upon its back and we

Will be upon our way.

★ COMIC NERD: ♥♥♥♥◗
★ STUBBLE: +5
★ eyes: ???

★ DRAW: yes
★ FITS INSIDE a DRYER: yes
★ INTERNET FAMOUS: kinda.

★ BREAKFAST: 24/7
★ exhIBITIONISM: 80%
★ SCOTT PILGRIM: TOTALLY

★ HEIGHT: THE TALLEST
★ MOOD: MILDLY ORNERY
★ WE'RE NOT: PAYING TO HEAT THE OUTSIDE what, were you born in a barn or someth:

is very quiet

★ LIKES YUKO: ♥♥♥♥♥
★ LIKES EVERYONE ELSE: ♥♥
★ MEOW: meow meow meow meow meow meow meow

we live in brooklyn.

prelude to a ballad

CMYcat

NOW ROOK IS

hand-face coordination

monochrome

WINTER

fwooo

SUMMER

AND SOON
ENOUGH

huh.

oh the horror

now we have to buy a new pork loin.

korra arms

ballad of laundry cat

terrible terrible food science

but in all seriousness

a secret for the ages

HOURLY COMICS

Hourly comics are comics drawn hour by hour over the course of a day. There's usually a designated date that everybody does them and in Yuko's case they usually span several pages, meaning they go onto the site as an extra tall comic. We've reformatted them to fit these pages more comfortably.

(Hourly comics are not to be confused with 24-hour comics, which are 24-page stories started and completed in a 24-hour period.)

hourly comics: february 1st, 2011

10:00 am

WAIT, TODAY IS HOURLY COMICS DAY?

tak tak

BUT I'M ALREADY DRAWING COMICS!

I'M DRAWING COMICS RIGHT NOW!

11:00 am

EATING CEREAL.

meow meow meow meow meow meow meow meow meow meow meow meow meow

ROOK WANTS TO LICK THE BOTTOM OF THE BOWL.

12:00 PM

WAS GOING TO MAKE THE BED, BUT THE CAT IS ASLEEP ON IT.

z

he looks like laundry.

1:00 PM

MY THROAT'S BUGGING ME, SO ANANTH MADE ME TEA.

SLPP

ONE OF THESE DAYS, I'M GOING TO ACCIDENTALLY DESTROY ALL OF MY COMICS.

like 20 pages of originals

2:00 PM

instant ramen ↓

leftover curry ↓

CURRY RAMEN

SSPLURP

stop that

I'm trying to get work done

3:00 PM

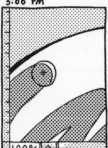

4:00 PM

5:00 PM

6:00 PM

7:00 PM

and then I went to bed.

extended ballad of laundry cat

kitten quarantine

LITTER

BEHIND THE TOILET

LITTER

IN THE SINK

LITTER

ON THE WALLS

LITTER

ON THE KITTEN

the return of sweetie pie

5 DAYS LATER:

speaking from experience

combustifier

KETCHUP.

GRAIN ALCOHOL.

PURE CESIUM

blacggle

THINGS THAT WOULD
PROBABLY MAKE THE
HUMIDIFIER CATCH FIRE

MR. BARGLES

should've taken the ferry

johnentines

you've exceeded my expectations, but they weren't high to begin with, valentine

I'm disappointed because I care, valentine

I lowered my standards just for you, valentine

Don't Fuck it up, valentine

let me rethink this

the surest path to friendship

1. APPROACH

2. ENGAGE

3. IGNORE

4. RUB ON SOME STUFF

5. ENGAGE AGAIN

6. IGNORE

the fiercest pokeyman

tick tick tick tick

excuse me sir, we can keep your luggage behind the counter.

OH, SURE.

anything in here, y'know, ticking or whatever?

JUST MY CLOCK COLLECTION.

what does it meeean

naming the kitten

AND SO:

octopuses, not octopi

I HATE OCTOPUSES.

AN ANIMAL THAT GROSS HAS NO BUSINESS BEING THAT SMART.

HOW TO DRAW CRICKET

① draw a circle

② add two triangles

③ and two smaller circles

④ draw an upside-down heart

⑤ add a cat body

⑥ yay

you're done!

Cricket

☆ small: 🐱🐱🐱
☆ cute: ♥♥♡♥♥
☆ smart: 💡🐱..

urgent matters

CAT REUNION

Once every year, Rook and Cricket come with us to Yuko's parents' place over Christmas and the New Year. Every year they remember it a little more and become a little more adventurous, and every year they get on a little better and a little more quickly with Mika and Gonta, Yuko's parents' cats. Mika is the boss, and ultimately takes the longest to, uh, come to an understanding. Rook and Cricket switch roles - in NY, Rook is the fretful one, but in NJ he becomes more adventurous. Cricket, on the other hand, becomes a lot more cautious. Cats ... go figure.

when rook met mika

when rook met gonta

maid of honor

don't get any ideas, mom

happy april fools

carnivore-blocked

almost

cake sagan

bargle

BROUGHT TO YOU BY ASIAN ALCOHOL INTOLERANCE

ASIAN ALCOHOL INTOLERANCE

Yuko's only had alcohol twice. The first time was mead and it ended poorly, but she thought it was an allergic reaction to sulfites. The experience was bad enough that she didn't try drinking again until years later. The second time she tried to finish half of a friend's soju cocktail - the Moonlight something Seoul Twilight something - and it ended up being much worse than the first time!

I decided to read up because her reaction was extremely strong and this is what I learned:

Alcohol intolerance isn't common, but appears with much greater frequency in people of Japanese, Chinese & Korean descent. Alcohol is processed by two enzymes in the liver. Enzyme 1, alcohol dehydrogenase, converts alcohol to acetaldehyde. Enzyme 2, aldehyde dehydrogenase, converts the acetaldehyde into acetic acid, which breaks down into harmless carbon dioxide and water. The process can take a long time if you drink a lot, but eventually the liver will metabolize it out.

People with alcohol intolerance have a genetic mutation that limits the production of Enzyme 2. As a result acetaldehyde builds up in the system in toxic quantities. It's the same as when someone drinks enough to make themselves sick, only people with alcohol intolerance get to that point much faster. The degree of a person's alcohol intolerance can vary widely - some people can handle a beer, some people can't even handle a sip.

The more you know ... !

thanks, nihilism dad

cat booger

drinking problem

watch your language

KIDS

Lela's specialty is kids! She worked at a day care for kids aged 2-4 for a while and she always brought stories back with her. Here are a few:

• The strongest child that Lela ever worked with was a 50-pound 4-year old. One time he decided it was time to go, so he got up and walked away ... with the stroller strapped to his back like a turtle shell.

• "Lela, you need to stop drinking coffee because your butt will get big."

• A 2-year old used to cryptically call the soap dispenser an "Occ-a-puss". It turned out he was trying to say the soap was like octopus ink.

• "Lela, your hair is like a big purple ice cream. Only I won't eat it."

• A little girl, when upset, would declare, "I am not a happy baby."

• One little girl is brushing another little girl's hair. They are trying to decide on a hair style. "Okay - so you want a teenager? OK, I will do a teenager."

the call is coming from inside the houussee

gas station snacks for dinner

SCUBA SHOP.

POTTERY STUDIO.

MASSAGE PARLOR.

WINERY.

WINERIES.

HORSELAND...
EMPORIUM...

EXOTIC MASSAGE PARLOR.

GRANITE SURFACING.

MASSAGE STUDIO...

"WITH ALL-ORIENTAL STAFF?"

WE FOUND EVERYTHING BUT FOOD.

where everybody knows your name

you know, those grey dogs with the impossible names

snickerdoggle

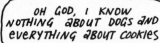

saxocat

puppy shower

YUKO, WILL YOU TEACH US HOW TO DRAW PUPPIES?

DRAWIN' PUPPIES

should have learned flag semaphore

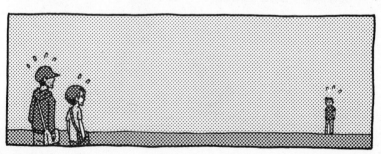

a few of my favorite things: TOUGH GUY EDITION

tough guy walking
girlfriend's dog

tough guy carrying
daughter's girly backpack

THAT WEIRD ECTO-COOLER SMOOTHIE THING THAT JOHN MAKES:

BLEND TOGETHER:

THE BETTER PART OF A 6 oz BAG OF FRESH SPINACH

10-15 FRESH MINT LEAVES

a HALF (or more) CAN OF FROZEN WHITE GRAPE JUICE CONCENTRATE

and a can of ginger ale if you want

then fill the blender with ice

and blend that, too

NO SERIOUSLY IT'S REALLY GOOD YOU GOTTA BELIEVE US

another day, another person mistaking yuko for a teenager

nope

good thing we just took up rock climbing

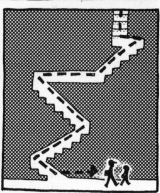

a few of my favorite things: SUBWAY MUSICIANS VERSION

FIVE-PIECE MARIACHI BAND IN FULL REGALIA

TIME-TRAVELING 80's RAPPER (surprisingly good!)

the time we drag-raced hulk hogan

cat ice tray

whew, that was a close one.

AND SOON:

not the first, not the last

- WASP STINGS: 0
- NEAR-DEATHS TANGENTIALLY CAUSED BY THE PRESENCE OF WASPS: MANY

every o'clock shadow

save yourself

ROCK CLIMBING

Rock climbing - more specifically bouldering - is our new favorite way to exercise. The place we go is a gym with faux rock walls. Different handholds of varying difficulty are arranged in routes that you have to climb. The routes are graded from V0 up to V12 and they get HARD! We've been there for a few months and are only now doing V3s.

Bouldering is as much a physical game as a mental game. Puzzling out the most efficient way up a wall - what holds to use, in what way to grasp them, how to position your body etc. - takes a lot of thought, especially as you graduate to higher difficulties. The way a person climbs can vary wildly too - it's often the case that the solution a taller person uses is different than that of a shorter person (height is not always advantageous!) and different kinds of strengths can yield radically different solutions too (core strength vs. upper body strength). And despite all of these differences, it's a great all-around workout that forces you to use the muscles in your body in a practical way.

The short version is: go try it out! And don't get discouraged by how bad you are ... grip strength is a big part of it and that takes a while to build up. You'll see!

stoppit, cat-dad

taking it off

lock your doors

uncharted

international man of mystery

MEANWHILE IN TAIPEI

magical buried treasure

chair sniper

seasonal prejudice

winter is coming

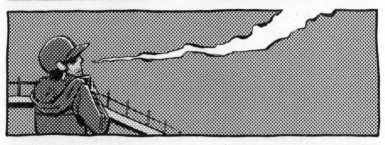

CHANGING SEASONS

My favorite season is Fall and my favorite times of year are the transition from Summer into Fall and the move from Fall into Winter. It's lovely watching the environment change naturally on such a grand scale. Also, admittedly, Fall is my favorite season for clothes - you can wear one jacket instead of your entire winter wardrobe every time you go out. Perfect weather.

why did they put them all next to each other

peanut blarghr

four-day conventionnnadfdgfds

DURATION OF WEEKEND

because we are in 3rd grade

all freight elevators are haunted

party cone

CRICKET GOT SPAYED LAST WEEK.

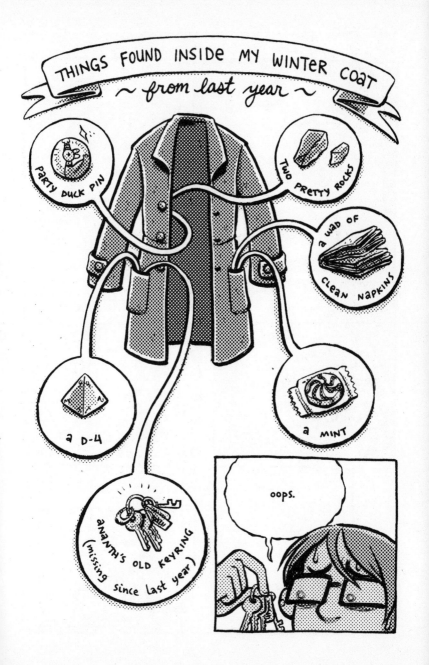

cat-rad

The Midas Touch

BUT WITH CAT HAIR

needs about ten packs of sugar

UNSWEETENED ICED COFFEE

ORDERED AN ICED CARAMEL MOCHA

guess I should drink it anyway .....

ssllllppp

AND THAT'S MY STORY.

I'M ... I'M SO PROUD

we are going to be best friends

it runs in the family

laundry rich

teeny fractal buddy

ch
ch
ch

IT...

IT LOOKS JUST LIKE A MANDELBROT SET...

I CAN'T WASH THAT OFF...

AND THEN MY DESK WAS NEVER CLEAN AGAIN.

yes

HI, ARE YOU—

...OVER 18?

YES.

YES, I'M 26.

OH! BECAUSE I COULD'VE SWORN YOU WERE 15.

I GET THAT A LOT.

YOU CAME TO THE DOOR AND I SWORE YOU WERE IN HIGH SCHOOL.

YES.

BECAUSE YOU LOOK LIKE A TEENAGER.

YES.

merry christmas, mom

LET'S MAKE A SANDWICH!

with yuko's dad

TAKE TWO SLICES OF LEFTOVER PIZZA

pepperoni

anchovy

COVER IN KIMCHI

KIMCHI

MICROWAVE

rrr

rrr

enjoy!

kitten of a hundred names

how can you be unhappy while wearing a cupcake hat

peppermint bargles

that's legal, right

c'mon I was checking my e-mail

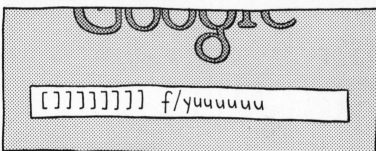

the worst place in the world

NIGHTMARE SQUARE

Times Sq. is a tourist attraction and a must-see ... so I'm going to let you down easy. Well, not really. It's dense with people and difficult to navigate. Here's a list of things I'd rather do than walk through Times Sq.:

- Climb the Empire State Building
- Fish in the Hudson
- Swim in the Gowanus
- High-five a sewer rat
- Dance on the 3rd rail
- Walk in the bike lane
- Bike in front of a cab
- Ride with a crazy cabbie
- Live inside the solar core

cat burglar in the making

and so :

tai chi-ing up the wall

water cat

shirt cat

punishment cat

on hubris

BUT THEN

taking compliments like a pro with yuko

bassinet chariot

schrodinger's book

ONE OF OUR MISSING BOXES ARRIVED!

oh.

THIS IS NOT OURS.

HOMEOPATHIC MEDICINE

this is not my beautiful box

hunger games

FRIENDS DON'T LET FRIENDS SHOP HUNGRY

greasy pizza bro

serious art discussions

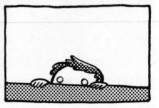

the urban climbing deer

inscrutable social rules

caldwell and the very medieval times birthday party

the most wonderful time of the year

noooooo

a funny thing happened on the way to the movies

with love from cat

a dangerous addiction

a pleasant drive

birthday cricket

kitten coda

HOW TO MAKE A
JOHNNY WANDER
COMIC

LET'S MAKE a JOHNNY WANDER COMIC!

or: how to make a Johnny Wander comic in 14 increasingly complex steps

①. write a script

1 Ananth is holding Cricket and she's yowling.
C: "NYAAOOOWWWWW"

2 Ananth puts her down and she immediately goes to sleep. (2 panels?)
A: "Do you think she remembers the laundromat? Growing up on the streets?"

3 They both look at Cricket sleeping.

4 Y: "I don't think she remembers the last five minutes."

End on a floating shot of Cricket being cute?

②. confer

hmm.

③. rewrite script

1 Ananth is holding Cricket and she's yowling.
C: "NYAAOOOWWWWW"

2 Ananth puts her down and she immediately goes to sleep. (2 panels?)
A: "How far back do you think she remembers?"

3 They both look at Cricket sleeping.
A: Do you think she remembers the laundromat?"

4 Y: "I don't think she remembers the last five minutes."

End on a floating shot of Cricket being cute.

4. draw a thumbnail

5. confer

hmm

6. redraw thumbnail

NYA

⑦. pencil the comic

.5 mechanical pencil

non-photo blue pencil lead*

some sorta eraser

clear ruler

7 x 10" spiral-bound sketchbook (acid free)

* non-photo blue lines do not show up in greyscale or b/w scans and thus do not have to be erased from finished art

⑧. edit

⑨ inks

.8mm felt pen
for panel borders

.3mm felt pen
for dialogue text

NYOOOOUU

DO YOU THINK
SHE REMEMBERS
THE LAUNDROMAT?

HOW FAR BACK
DO YOU THINK
SHE REMEMBERS?

I DON'T THINK SHE
REMEMBERS THE
LAST FIVE MINUTES.

fine Japanese calligraphy pen
for everything else

⑩ scan*

bbbrrr rrnn

* I scan in grayscale at 600DPI

LINEWORK LAYER

linework should be
set to "multiply"

⑪ add grey tones

50% GREY LAYER

All tones should be
underneath the linework

30% GREY LAYER

10% GREY LAYER

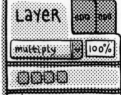

LAYER

multiply   100%

 LINEWORK

 50% GREY

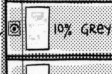 30% GREY

 10% GREY

BACKGROUND

Please note: Work area
is based on Photoshop

⑫ OK LET'S MAKE HALFTONES

MAKE 3 NEW GREYSCALE FILES WITH A SOLID GREY FILL, LIKE THIS:

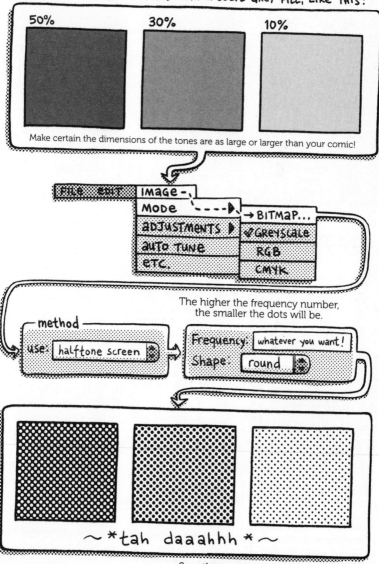

50%

30%

10%

Make certain the dimensions of the tones are as large or larger than your comic!

FILE EDIT | IMAGE
MODE → BITMAP...
ADJUSTMENTS ✓ GREYSCALE
AUTO TUNE RGB
ETC. CMYK

The higher the frequency number,
the smaller the dots will be.

— method —
use: halftone screen

Frequency: whatever you want!
Shape: round

~*tah daaahhh*~

Save these so you can re-use them later!

⑬ NOW LET'S MAKE a CLIPPING LayER

COPY & PaSTE THE 50% HALFTONE INTO a NEW LayER aBOVE 50% GREY

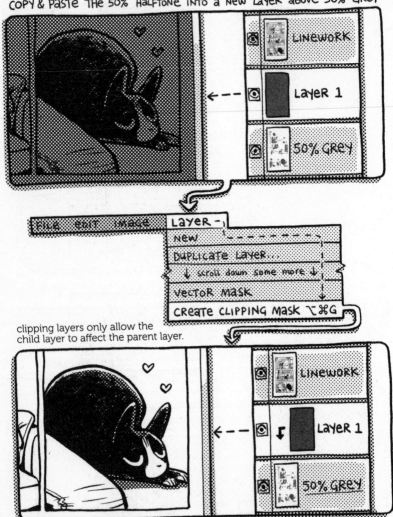

FILE   EDIT   IMAGE | LayER →
                          NEW   - - - - - - -
                          DUPLICATE LayER...
                          ↓ scroll down some more ↓
                          VECTOR MASK
                          CREATE CLIPPING MASK ⌥⌘G

clipping layers only allow the
child layer to affect the parent layer.

now repeat for 30% and 10% grey

LOOKIT THAT HANDSOME FINISHED COMIC!

NAME Yuko
ZODIAC SIGN Ox
ASTROLOGICAL SIGN Taurus
BLOOD TYPE Rose Red
HOBBIES Leaving love letters in Ananth-sempai's locker, going to high school under the pretense of being a boy.
FAVORITE FOODS Very Rare Steak, Coffee
LEAST FAVORITE FOODS Marshmallow

"WORK VERY HARD!"

YUKO OTA is a cartoonist & illustrator who has worked with publishers like Oni Press, Dark Horse Inc., Lerner Publishing, BOOM!, Benign Kingdom and Red5 on properties including Adventure Time, Yo Gabba Gabba, Atomic Robo & more. She lives somewhere in Brooklyn, NY and works in a tiny home office, where she wages a never-ending war with two cats for possession of her chair.

Yuko spent part of her high school career masquerading as a boy. She found herself at the center of a complex love polygon, but she left all those boys behind and married comics instead.

NAME Ananth
ZODIAC SIGN Boar
ASTROLOGICAL SIGN Libra
BLOOD TYPE Sakura Scarlet
HOBBIES Standing under the cherry blossoms in Spring as they bloom in the wind while his heart pounds faster still.
FAVORITE FOODS Sweet Coffee
LEAST FAVORITE FOODS Potato

"I WOULD DATE WITH YOU"

ANANTH PANAGARIYA is a writer, designer and reader who has written and produced work for Oni Press, First Second, Dark Horse, Inc, and Benign Kingdom, including comics, t-shirt & ad design and production work. He has done design and brand identity for Silicon Valley start-ups including Snapture, an iPhone app featured in the pages of WIRED, BBC, Forbes, New York Times, and the Wall Street Journal. He writes constantly, and is usually putting pencil to paper, analog or otherwise.

Ananth was a bad seed in his youth and has vowed to spend the rest of his life making up for it, by fighting on the side of justice.

OTHER WORK BY THE AUTHORS

Johnny Wander Volume 1: Don't Burn The House Down
ISBN-10 0978501616, ISBN-13 978-0978501617

Johnny Wander Volume 2: Escape to New York
ISBN-10 0978501624, ISBN-13 978-0978501624

Johnny Wander Volume 3: Ballad of Laundry Cat
ISBN-10 0978501648, ISBN-13 978-0978501648

The Bootlegger in Marceline & The Scream Queens #4 from BOOM!

Callie Eats Feathers in MDHP Vol. 5 from Dark Horse Comics
ISBN-10 1595825703, ISBN-13 978-1595825704

YUKO

Revenge of Dr. Dinosaur in Atomic Robo: Real Science Adventures #1 from Red5

Spring 2012 Art Book: Yuko Ota from Benign Kingdom

My Boyfriend is a Monster 8: A Match Made in Heaven from Lerner Publishing
HARDCOVER ISBN-13 978-076136857-1 PAPERBACK ISBN-13 978-1467707329

Manga Math Mysteries 3: The Secret Ghost from Lerner Publishing
ISBN-10 0761352457 ISBN-13 978-0761352457

Twisted Journeys: Detective Frankenstein from Lerner Publishing
ISBN-10 0822589435 ISBN-13 978-0822589433

Yo Gabba Gabba: Comic Book Time from Oni Press
ISBN-10 1934964492 ISBN-13 978-1934964491

ANANTH

Applegeeks Volume 1 from Dark Horse Comics
ISBN-10 1595821740, ISBN-13 978-1595821744

Applegeeks Volume 2 from Dark Horse Comics
ISBN-10 1595823379, ISBN-13 978-1595823373

Robro in MDHP Vol. 4 from Dark Horse Comics
ISBN-10 1595823271 ISBN-13 978-1595823274

COMING SOON

BUZZ! from Oni Press
Lucky Penny from Oni Press

... and more! Catch up at johnnywander.com!